Edition Schott

Clarinet Library · Klarinetten-Bibliothek

Jörg Widmann

* 1973

Fantasie

für Klarinette in B solo
for Clarinet in B♭ solo

(1993, rev. 2011)

KLB 56
ISMN 979-0-001-13718-8

 **SCHOTT**

www.schott-music.com

Mainz · London · Berlin · Madrid · New York · Paris · Prague · Tokyo · Toronto
© 2005 SCHOTT MUSIC GmbH & Co. KG, Mainz · Printed in Germany

Aufführungshinweis:
Die Charakterwechsel, gerade auch auf engstem Raum,
sollen das ganze Stück hindurch sehr schroff und scharf gezeichnet sein.
Vorzeichen gelten nur für eine Note

Performance notice:
The changes of characters, especially between short phrases,
shall be profiled in a very abrupt and strict manner during the whole piece.
Accidentals apply to one note only.

Aufführungsdauer / Duration: 7'

Fantasie

Frei, rhapsodisch / _Free, rhapsodically_

Jörg Widmann
*1973

Tempo, grazioso
schlicht, quasi Ländler
simple, quasi Ländler

quasi
„erschrocken" / _'frightened'_

Multiphonic
come prima

Alpenländisch, tänzerisch
with an Alpine feel, like a dance

*) aber F-Griff von Multphonic übernehmen / _but take over fingering of the multiphonic_
**) Synonymtriller mit r. Hd. kl. Finger, obere Klappe / _Synonym Trill with r. h. little finger, upper key_
***) langsam beginnen, schneller werden / _start trill slowly, accelerate_

Das widerrechtliche Kopieren von Noten ist gesetzlich
verboten und kann privat–und strafrechtlich verfolgt werden.
Unauthorised copying of music is forbidden by law,
and may result in criminal or civil action.

© 2005 Schott Music GmbH & Co. KG, Mainz

51 573

*) sehr leiser Klarinettenton, aber **ff**-Klappengeräusche / *very low clarinet sound, but **ff**-key noise*
   Die angegebenen Töne so schnell wie möglich chromatisch verbinden. / *Link   the indicated notes chromatically as fast as possible.*
**) Immer in Bewegung, etwas drängend, nie wie eine bloße Etüde abspulen. / *Constantly in motion, slightly forward moving, never rattling off like a*
   mere study.

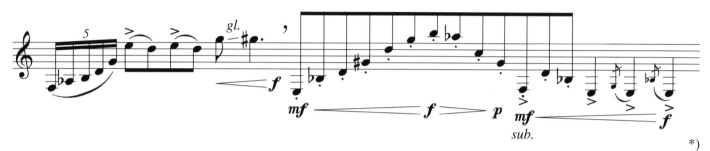

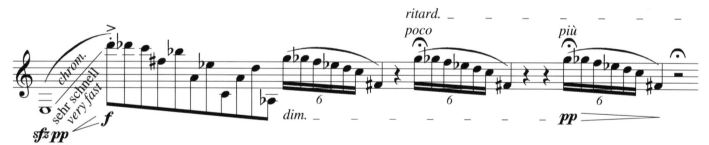

*) Wiederholung ad libitum / *Repetition ad libitum*

langsam ins Tempo
zurückkommen
gradually return to tempo

a tempo

Presto poss. *sub.*

accel. _ _ ritard. _

plötzlich viel
langsamer, über-
trieben jazzig
suddenly much slower,
exaggeratedly „jazzy"

Presto possibile subito
(plötzlicher Charakterwechsel)
(sudden change of character)

Multiphonic
come prima

Tempo come prima, ma poco più mosso
Alpenländisch, tänzerisch
with an Alpine feel, like a dance

Multiphonic
come prima

glissando viel flüchtiger als zuvor
glissando much hastier than before

doloroso

viel flüchtiger als beim ersten Auftreten
much more fugitive than in the first appearance

staccatiss.
presto possibile

rit. molto

*) quasi Synonymtriller nach unten mit Zeigefinger rechts / *quasi synonym trill downwards with right index finger*
**) aber wie zu Anfang F-Griff von Multiphonic übernehmen / *but take over the fingering of the multiphonic as at the beginning*
***) Gabel-F + innere der 2 oberen Klappen (linker kleiner Finger) / *fork F + the inner of the 2 higher keys (left hand little finger)*
****) sehr perkussiv, quasi pianissimo-slaps / *very percussionlike, quasi pianissimo slaps*

Schnell, brillant (noch schneller und drängender als zuvor)
Fast, brilliant (even faster and more forward-pressing than before)

*) insgesamt steigern und cresc. bis vorletzte Zeile / generally intensify and cresc. up to the penultimate line

Schott Music, Mainz 51 573